BOOK 6

MASTER YOUR SPELLING

Geoff Davies
Sue Dillon
and
Terry Dillon

STANLEY
THORNES

First edition published in 1983 by
Basil Blackwell Ltd

Second edition published in 1993 by
Simon & Schuster Education

Reprinted in 1994

Reprinted in 1995 by
Stanley Thornes Publishers Ltd
Ellenborough House
Wellington Street
Cheltenham GL50 1YD

A catalogue record of this book is available from the British
Library.

ISBN 0 7487 2489 3

Design and typesetting by Can Do Design
Illustrated by Roger Backwell
Printed in the United Kingdom by Redwood Books, Trowbridge

Contents

How to Master your Spelling

To learn the words in this book:

do the activities.

Then, for each word you don't already know well:

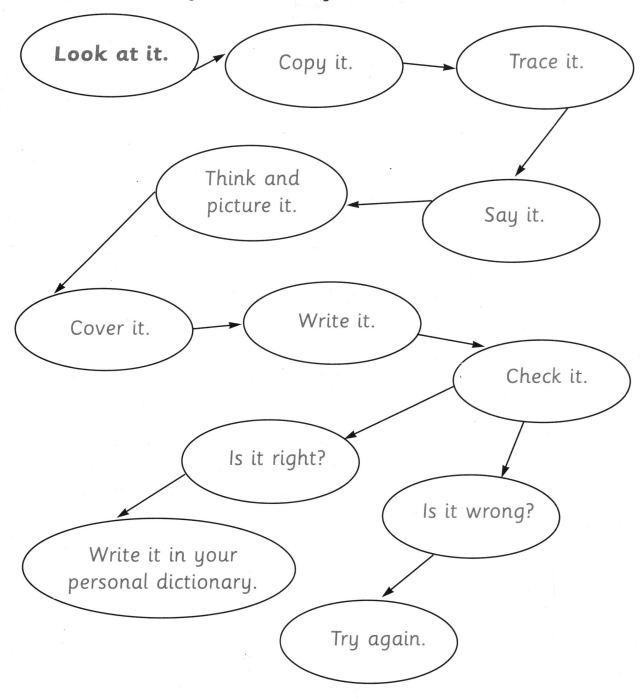

Look at it. → Copy it. → Trace it.

Say it. → Think and picture it.

Cover it. → Write it. → Check it.

Is it right? Is it wrong?

Write it in your personal dictionary.

Try again.

Looking back

1 Use the words in the box to complete the sentences below. Write out the sentences in your book. Record words for your personal files if you need to do so.

a Judge Smart had no a _ _ _ _ _ _ _ _ e but to send him to prison.

b The officer said he had a w _ _ _ _ _ t for Mary's arrest.

c Be c _ _ _ _ _ l not to damage this u _ _ _ _ e papyrus.

d The first a _ _ _ _ _ _ _ t was Yuri Gagarin in 1961.

e Crippen was charged with m _ _ _ _ r and not ma _ _ _ _ u _ _ _ _ r.

f We can thank Freud for the science of ps _ _ _ _ _ _ _ y.

g The first g _ _ _ _ _ s may have come from India in the 15th c _ _ _ _ _ y.

h Smashing that window was a d _ _ _ _ _ _ _ te act of vandalism.

i Everything in the room was blown to sm _ _ _ _ _ ee _ _ in the explosion.

**alternative   astronaut   careful   century
deliberate   gypsies   manslaughter   murder
psychology   smithereens   unique   warrant**

Back tracking

1 Find the definitions of the clues below.

    a tennis bat, spelt two ways   r _ _ _ _ _ _   or _ _ _ _ _ _

    b British that preceded the
         Commonwealth   E _ _ _ _ _

    c opposite of multiplication   d _ _ _ _ _ _ _

    d another word for bravery   v _ _ _ _ _

    e gloomy   d _ _ _ _ _

    f people next door   n _ _ _ _ _ _ _ _

> **dismal   division   Empire   neighbours
> racquet or racket   valour**

2 Write out the long sentence below and insert the correct words. All the words in **bold** in this sentence end in **able** or **ible**.

The police **co** _ _ _ _ _ _ _ was called to the scene of the **ho** _ _ _ _ _ _ murder and, although a **re** _ _ _ _ _ _ witness, who had some **se** _ _ _ _ _ _ things to say and could probably offer **va** _ _ _ _ _ _ evidence, was **av** _ _ _ _ _ _ _ , it was not **po** _ _ _ _ _ to believe that the **te** _ _ _ _ _ _ deed could have been committed by an **in** _ _ _ _ _ _ _ man, the subject of a story written by H. G. Wells.

> **available   constable   horrible
> invisible   possible   reliable   sensible
> terrible   valuable**

6

Another look back

1 The words in **bold** below have been put in the wrong
sentences. Write out the sentences with the correct words.

  a Look in a **altitude** to find the meaning of a word.

  b Hold the cover in place with an **efficiently** band.

  c The repair was done quickly and **inquisitive**.

  d The day trip was an **dictionary** disaster.

  e At high **opportunity**, mountaineers must breathe
    oxygen.

  f The Marines led the **intermittent** with its drum
    corps.

  g The **parade** monkey got its hand stuck in the pot.

  h If you get the **antiseptic** to go, then take it.

  i The stranded ship blew **elastic** blasts on its siren.

  j The first **absolute** was carbolic acid.

2 In reverse

If 26 = a, 25 = b, 24 = c, 23 = d and so on to 3 = x,
2 = y and 1 = z, what are the following words? Write
them in your book when you have broken the code.

    a 12 : 9 : 11 : 19 : 26 : 13

    b 26 : 11 : 11 : 15 : 18 : 24 : 26 : 7 : 18 : 12 : 13

    c 24 : 26 : 11 : 8 : 18 : 1 : 22

    d 26 : 13 : 26 : 15 : 2 : 8 : 22

    e 26 : 13 : 26 : 15 : 2 : 8 : 18 : 8

    f 8 : 6 : 25 : 8 : 7 : 26 : 13 : 7 : 18 : 26 : 15

    g 7 : 22 : 9 : 9 : 18 : 7 : 12 : 9 : 2

Apostrophe refresher

There is no mystery about the use of apostrophes.

Simply — An apostrophe is used to show that something has been left out.

For example: **I'm** is short for **I am**. The apostrophe stands for the **a** in **am**.

and — I **can't** is short for I **cannot**. The apostrophe stands for the **no** in **cannot**.

but — I **shall not** is shortened to I **shan't** (not sha'n't).

and — I **will not** is shortened to I **won't** (because **will** used to be spelt **wol**).

1 Use an apostrophe to replace one, two, three or four of the letters in the words in **bold** below. Write out the sentences in your book.

a you **must not** argue   e **I shall** scream

b **he will** come   f **you have** missed

c **she would** cry   g you **have not** lost it

d she **would not** cry   h **there would** be no answer

2 Apostrophes are **never** used to make **plurals**.

For example: **potato's** is wrong   **potatoes** is right

                  boot's is wrong   **boots** is right

Correct the apostrophe errors below by writing down the correct plural for each word.

a tomato's   d toe's   g army's

b witch's   e horses'   h trophy's

c duck's   f piano's   i shelf's

Silent letters review

1 Replace the * in each of the words below with the correct silent letter or letters. Write them in your book.

a ag * ast

b as * ertain

c as * ma

d bus * ness

e bus * le

f deli * t

g des * end

h disg * ise

i dou * t

j epis * le

k fr * end

l * narled

m h * i * t

n hym *

o je * lousy

p * no * ledge

q le * sure

r morg *

s * neumonia

t re * koning

u resi * ned

v s * issors

w ste * dfast

x thro * t

y tom * stone

z vag *

ac

1 Solve the clues below.

Begin with the missing **ac** and end with the letter in **bold**. The unscrambled words are in the box.

a bitter about something — suoinomir**r**

b agree easily — secuqie

c spirit vinegar — iect **d**i

d smoke to make your eyes smart — idr

e spots and pimples on the face — en

f from which grow all great oaks — rno

g to do with sound — usotc**i**

h obtain something — ureqi

i not to be forgot in '*Auld Lang Syne*' — cuauqetnnai

j imperial measure of area — er

k make it known you've been helped — ageklonwd

l found 'not guilty' and released — uatqti**l**

m what you obtained — siiiotun**q**

> **acetic   acid   acknowledge   acne   acorn
> acoustic   acquaintance   acquiesce   acquire
> acquisition   acquittal   acre   acrid
> acrimonious**

---

2 This is an **acronym**: N. E. W. S. It stands for 'Never Expect Wet Summers'. Invent at least three acronyms of your own.

an

1 All the words below should begin with **an**, but
the beginnings are missing. Complete the words.

a droid   **e** alogy

b thology   **f** tediluvian

c imation   **g** ecdote

d agram   **h** achronism

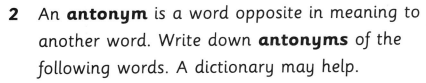

2 An **antonym** is a word opposite in meaning to
another word. Write down **antonyms** of the
following words. A dictionary may help.

a anxious   **d** anonymous

b ancient   **e** anybody

c angular   **f** antagonist

3 Sewn is an **anagram** of news. Make **anagrams** of
the following words.

a angelic   **c** antagonise   **e** antecedent

b annihilate   **d** anaesthetic   **f** antiquated

4 The two sentences below contain **anachronisms**.
Explain the word **anachronism**.

a Robin Hood heard the Sheriff threaten him on local radio.

b William Shakespeare stole the plot and recorded it on tape.

Write three anachronisms of your own.

as au

1 **as** is missing from the beginning of the words below.
   Re-attach the letters and complete the words.

   a fireproof, but is harmful to health   bestos
   b sanctuary   ylum
   c pain-killer   pirin
   d small planet   teroid
   e used to surface roads   phalt
   f suffocation   phyxia
   g what this is called *   terisk

2 The words below all begin with **au**, shown by
   this symbol <>. Complete the words and record
   them in your book. The numbers in brackets tell you
   how many letters there are in the complete word.

   a daring and bold   <> dac . . s (9)
   b to do with sound   <> d . . (5)
   c person who examines accounts <> d . . r (7)
   d to increase and add to   <> gm . . (7)
   e harsh and stern   <> s . e . . (7)

audacious   audio   auditor
augment   austere

12

mn ph pn rh

1 Solve the clues below. Write out the answers and write a short sentence about each word to explain what it means.

a stalks used as fruit   rh _ _ _ _ b

b make music on one with wooden hammers   xy _ _ _ _ _ ne

c large thick-skinned animal   rh _ _ _ _ _ _ _ s

d an emotional piece of music   rh _ _ _ _ _ y

e a muscular disease   rh _ _ m _ _ _ _ m

f it surrounds the Earth   at _ _ s _ _ _ _ e

g diamond shape   rh _ _ _ _ s

h has no mother or father   o _ _ _ _ n

i an evergreen flowering shrub   rh _ _ od _ _ _ _ _ n

j very serious   sol _ _ _

k musical beat   rh _ _ _ m

l tyre filled with air   pn _ _ m _ _ _ c

m South American dance   rh _ _ _ a

n lives on land and in water   am _ _ _ bi _ n

o serious lung disease   pn _ _ _ _ _ ia

p sacred song   h _ _ n

q what 'June', 'moon' and 'soon' all do   rh _ _ e

r sentence to severe punishment   co _ _ _ _ n

s Nelson stands on his in Trafalgar Square   co _ _ _ n

t follows summer   a _ _ _ _ n

13

ae eo eu eau

1 Use the code to work out the words below. Write them in your own collection.

If][= ae   <> = eo   >< = eu and * = eau

a][roplane

b][rial

c lunch <> n

d][rated

e l <> tard

f f >< dal

g b * tiful

h pig <> n

i li >< tenant

j Bur *

k surg <> n

l dung <> n

m f >< d

n][robics

o trunch <> n

p an][sthetic

2 Complete the sentences below. Write them out in your book.

a Charles has been promoted to captain from l _ _ _ _ _ _ _ _ t.

b The senior s _ _ g _ _ n will operate on the patient early tomorrow.

c The captive was flung into a filthy d _ _ g _ _ n.

d F. B. I. stands for the Federal B _ r _ _ u of investigation.

e The policeman hit him hard with the t _ _ nc _ _ _ n.

f Katherine needs a new l _ o _ _ _ d for her a _ _ ob _ _ s classes.

g Make sure that your a _ _ _ _ _ l is ozone-friendly.

pre

1 Use **pre** to complete all the part-words below.

a _ _ _ caution   **d** _ _ _ stige

b _ _ _ servation   **e** _ _ _ sume

c _ _ _ sident   **f** _ _ _ tence

2 Use the clues to help you to unscramble the words below. They begin with **pre** and end with the letter **in bold**.

a The chest was full of _ _ _ _ _ _ _ _ stones.   **suicpreo**

b The girl is _ _ _ _ _ _ _ _ and the baby is due soon.   **tnngprea**

c Get my _ _ _ _ _ _ _ _ _ _ _ _ from the pharmacist, please.   **n**tscpiprerio

d _ _ _ _ _ _ _ _ _ _ is better than a cure.   it**ne**Preonv

e When the baby was born it was a month _ _ _ _ _ _ _ _ .   mtapre**e**ru

f The lens must be ground with absolute _ _ _ _ _ _ _ _ .   **n**preoscii

g The houses were _ _ _ _ _ _ _ _ _ _ _ _ in a factory.   **d**eaafprebrict

h The climber fell over the _ _ _ _ _ _ _ _ _ and died.   eiiprepc**c**

i Install alarm systems in all _ _ _ _ _ _ _ _ .   miepres**s**

j Kneel in the _ _ _ _ _ _ _ _ of the emperor.   eesprec**n**

pro

1 Find the thirteen **pro** words in this grid. The words run in all directions.

f	p	r	o	d	i	g	y	e	m
p	r	o	p	a	g	a	n	d	a
r	k	p	r	o	f	i	t	a	r
o	p	r	o	d	u	c	t	n	g
b	r	o	b	e	d	x	z	e	o
a	o	p	l	j	b	w	h	m	r
t	o	h	e	w	q	o	g	o	p
i	f	e	m	k	m	z	r	r	w
o	y	t	r	e	p	o	r	p	z
n	o	i	s	s	e	c	o	r	p

NEWSAGENT

2 The words in **bold** below have been put in the wrong sentences. Write out the sentences with the correct words.

a In all **proficiency** we will come with you.

b Measure the angle with your **proportion**.

c Have you passed your cycle **proprietor** test?

d Only a **probability** of the prisoners escaped.

e The **proverb** of the shop says he has been robbed.

f Tanya is to be a witness for the **protractor**.

g 'Look before you leap' is an old **profession**.

h Matthew is training to join the legal **prosecution**.

art can dir men

1 Re-attach the missing beginnings to the words below.

art can dir men sen viv

a did
b efact
c tankerous
d ectory
e sation
f tality
g suration
h didate
i ection
j ister
k yon
l ector
m sitive

n cellation
o nibal
p acious
q id
r timental
s ificial
t tion
u struation
v ective
w iority
x sor
y cel

2 **Dir** assignment: Write three sentences to explain the difference between:

a a directive,
b a director,
c a directory.

3 **Men** assignment: Write two sentences to explain the difference between:

a menstruation,
b mensuration.

Prefixes - Greek influence

The following prefixes come from the ancient Greek language.

astro comes from the Greek word for **star**
bio comes from the Greek word for **life**
electro comes from the Greek word for **amber**

1 These prefixes also come from Greek words.

geo heli mono phil photo stereo therm theo

Attach the correct prefix to the part-words below.

a	ometer	**d**	logy	**g**	copter
b	naut	**e**	graphy	**h**	osophy
c	nic	**f**	dolite	**i**	plane

2 Find the words with prefixes that come from Greek words.

a	metropolitan	**e**	antidote	**i**	biceps
b	microscope	**f**	photograph	**j**	viaduct
c	chronicle	**g**	automatic	**k**	biopsy
d	diameter	**h**	petroleum	**l**	philately

3 a Write two sentences to explain the difference between **astrology** and **astronomy** (look at page 35).

(look at page 35).

   b Write a sentence to explain what is meant by **philately**.

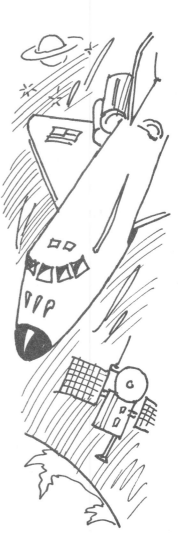

Word mix

1 Complete the sentences below. Choose the words from the box and write out the sentences in your book.

a Both tea and coffee contain c _ _ _ _ _ _ e.

b She is showing all the s _ _ _ _ _ _ _ of influenza.

c Percy has a g _ _ _ _ _ _ _ _ n appetite.

d The n _ _ _ _ _ _ e in cigarettes is very harmful.

e Nicotine is used as a p _ _ _ _ _ _ _ e.

f Some British newspapers are called the 't _ _ _ _ _ d press'.

g Can I have the r _ _ _ _ e for that cake?

h The rash keeps r _ _ _ _ _ _ _ g and the treatment is useless.

i Kingsley Amis is a popular c _ _ _ _ _ _ _ _ _ _ y author.

j Grandad gets very n _ _ _ _ _ _ _ c about his home town.

k Poppy uses too much m _ _ _ _ _ a as eye make-up.

l Chocolate is made from c _ _ _ _ beans.

m George wants e _ _ _ _ c groups to be represented at the meeting.

> **caffeine   cocoa   contemporary   ethnic**
> **gargantuan   mascara   nicotine**
> **nostalgic   pesticide   recipe   recurring**
> **symptoms   tabloid**

Prefixes – Latin influence

Many English words have prefixes that come from Latin.

trans   comes from the Latin word for **across**
contra   comes from the Latin word for **against**
civi   comes from the Latin word for **citizen**

1 Use prefixes to complete the sentences below. Write
them in your book.

a Pete put up a ma _ _ _ _ _ _ _ _ fight but
had to surrender.
b It would take a huge mo _ _ _ _ _ _ to buy that
cottage.
c The dentist prodded at the c _ _ _ _ _ in my tooth.
d The woman collapsed after a co _ _ _ _ _ _ arrest.
e Every swing of the pe _ _ _ _ _ _ brings the
dreaded day closer.
f The driver completely ignored the pe _ _ _ _ _ _ _ _
crossing.

2 The prefixes in the words below have become confused.
Correct them and file the new words you make.

a lunelty   d matimen   g perficine
b maloration   e novignant   h specipulate
c medernity   f manacy

---

cavity coronary lunacy magnificent
malignant manipulate maternity
medicine mortgage novelty pedestrian
pendulum perforation specimen

Word mix 2

1 Use the words in the box to complete the sentences below.

a The roar from the motor-cycle's _ xh _ _ _ _ was deafening.

b The m _ _ _ _ _ o _ is a race of over 40km.

c The makeshift tent d _ s _ _ _ _ _ _ _ _ _ d during the storm.

d The drums rolled in a cr _ _ _ _ _ _ o as the axe fell.

e You can buy those shoes in the sports d _ _ _ r _ _ _ _ _ .

f Sixty boats took part in the annual r _ _ _ t _ _ .

g The group discussed the advantages of both c _ _ _ _ e _ _ _ _ _ _ _ and grammar schools.

h The m _ _ _ _ n _ _ helps you to remember words.

i The water was polluted by a discharge of e _ _ _ u _ _ _ .

j Word blindness is usually called d _ _ _ _ x _ _ .

k The author was offended by the mildest cr _ _ _ _ _ _ _ .

l The 100m crawl was the last event in the swimming g _ _ _ .

m The driver was caught tipping t _ _ _ _ waste.

> **comprehensive crescendo criticism
> department disintegrated dyslexia
> effluent exhaust gala marathon
> mnemonic regatta toxic**

Plurals

Some nouns do not change at all when
they become plural (more than one).
Some nouns have no plural at all.

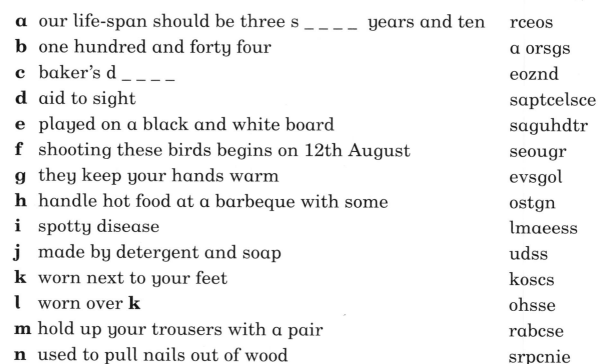

1 Use the clues to find the words.

a our life-span should be three s _ _ _ _ years and ten   rceos

b one hundred and forty four   a orsgs

c baker's d _ _ _ _   eoznd

d aid to sight   saptcelsce

e played on a black and white board   saguhdtr

f shooting these birds begins on 12th August   seougr

g they keep your hands warm   evsgol

h handle hot food at a barbeque with some   ostgn

i spotty disease   lmaeess

j made by detergent and soap   udss

k worn next to your feet   koscs

l worn over **k**   ohsse

m hold up your trousers with a pair   rabcse

n used to pull nails out of wood   srpcnie

2 Complete the sentences below by unscrambling
the words in **bold**.

a Cut out the pattern with a pair of **ssssroic**.

b **rrgneHi** are smoked to make kippers.

c Uncle trimmed the hedge with a pair of **rshesa**.

d John needs a new pair of riding- **oostb**.

e Let us give **skntah** for all that we have.

f Get a grip on the wire with a pair of **eisrlp**.

Word mix 3

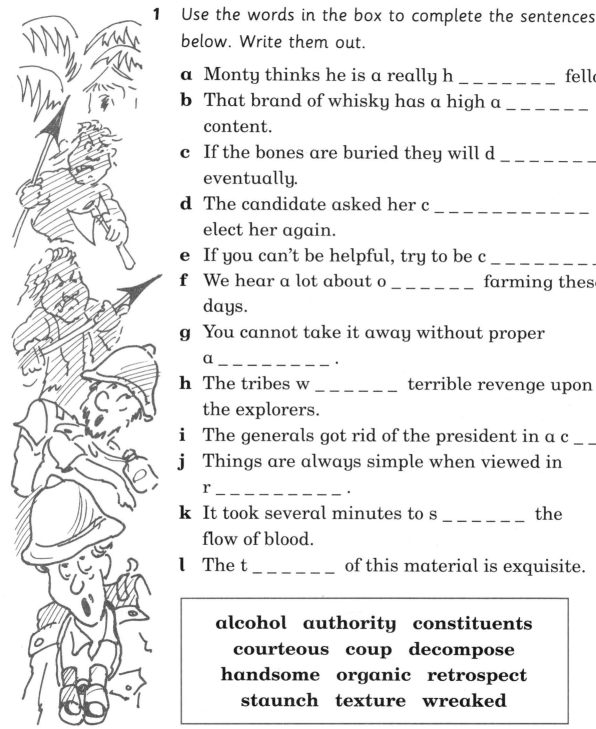

1 Use the words in the box to complete the sentences below. Write them out.

a Monty thinks he is a really h _ _ _ _ _ _ fellow.

b That brand of whisky has a high a _ _ _ _ _ _ content.

c If the bones are buried they will d _ _ _ _ _ _ _ _ eventually.

d The candidate asked her c _ _ _ _ _ _ _ _ _ _ _ to elect her again.

e If you can't be helpful, try to be c _ _ _ _ _ _ _ _ .

f We hear a lot about o _ _ _ _ _ _ farming these days.

g You cannot take it away without proper a _ _ _ _ _ _ _ _ .

h The tribes w _ _ _ _ _ _ terrible revenge upon the explorers.

i The generals got rid of the president in a c _ _ _ .

j Things are always simple when viewed in r _ _ _ _ _ _ _ _ _ .

k It took several minutes to s _ _ _ _ _ _ the flow of blood.

l The t _ _ _ _ _ _ of this material is exquisite.

alcohol authority constituents
courteous coup decompose
handsome organic retrospect
staunch texture wreaked

Nouns to adjectives

Many nouns do not follow a set rule when they are changed into adjectives.

1 Match the adjectives in the box to the nouns.

a	ability	**h**	anxiety	**o**	decency
b	accuracy	**i**	scenery	**p**	vanity
c	simplicity	**j**	reality	**q**	wit
d	circle	**k**	voice	**r**	shortage
e	energy	**l**	poverty	**s**	laughter
f	ferocity	**m**	justice	**t**	prosperity
g	decision	**n**	cruelty		

> **able   accurate   anxious   circular   cruel
> decent   decisive   energetic   fierce   just
> laugh   poor   prosperous   real   scenic
> short   simple   vain   vocal   witty**

2 Look in a dictionary to find the matching adjectives for the nouns below.

a	allergy	**g**	knowledge
b	error	**h**	space
c	joint	**i**	zeal
d	nerve	**j**	cleanliness
e	vacancy	**k**	habit
f	bacteria	**l**	quarrel

Words and music

1 Solve the clues.

a opposite of harmony   osdicdr

b very high adult male voice sounding unnatural   lattfseo

c modern rhythm and blues music   orkc dna lorl

d song performed by two people   utde

e song telling a story   ldbaal

f lowest female voice   rntcoaolt

g used by a conductor   nbota

h 'God save the Queen' is our national   thnmae

i played by trumpets to announce arrival   arfnfae

j popular music that began in New Orleans   zjza

k instrumental solo such as Chopin's 'Moonlight'   notsaa

l sung Mass for the dead   qieurme

m high bass male voice   rtbele

n Swiss singing with natural and falsetto voice   elydo

o highest male voice   enrot

p sung drama   raoep

---

anthem ballad baton contralto
discord duet falsetto fanfare jazz
opera requiem rock and roll sonata
tenor treble yodel

Words used in grammar

abbreviation adjective adverb
antonym bracket colon & semicolon
comma conjunctions diminutive
exclamation mark feminine (gender)
homonym masculine (gender)
metaphor neuter (gender)
onomatopoeia phrase preposition
pronoun simile synonym

1 Match each of the grammar words in the box to an example below. Each matching has a clue to help you. You may have to do some research.

a and but

b !

c toot toot! boom boom!

d boy

e softly

f B. B. C.

g lambkin

h a lost cause

i duchess

j ,

k table

l them

m {} () []

n gorgeous

o : ;

p up and down

q hour and our

r happy and glad

s he is a real star

t as soft as silk

u on over behind

The theatre

1 The words in **bold** below have been put in the wrong sentences. Write out the sentences with the correct words.

a The **prompter** told some terrible jokes.

b The **encore** playing to the queue was a good musician.

c Daisy was very nervous at the **limelight** she attended.

d The audience clamoured for an **overture**.

e The **curtain** made us all think he had disappeared.

f Fluffy forgot her lines and the **finale** was asleep!

g The audience was glad when the final **audition** fell.

h Shouting from the **illusionist** disrupted the show.

i The **gallery** was the most spectacular part of the show.

j The star will stay in the **busker** if you let him.

k The orchestra started the **comedian** before we were ready.

2 Break the code to find the words. Start each word with the letter(s) in **bold**.

a era**op**

b enium**prosc**

c ssionist**impre**

d pet**pup**

e nette**marion**

f aint**greasep**

g ge**dytra**

h **pt**scri

i tick**slaps**

j r**study**unde

k loquist**ventri**

l tine**rou**

Plurals - Latin influence

1 If <> = a :   >< = ae :   * = e :   ][= i :   }{ = im :
@ = x, work out the plurals of the following part-words.

a phenomen <>
b strat <>
c impediment <>
d radi][
e oas * s
f gymnasi <>
g errat <>
h plateau @
i ax * s
j fung][
k curricul <>

l optim <>
m seraph }{
n octop][
o bureau @
p rostr <>
q flor ><
r cherub }{
s formul ><
t polyhedr <>
u syllab][
v platyp][

Some of these words have simpler plurals.
Use a dictionary to find out what they are.

Gain a letter, lose a letter

Gain a letter

Some words **gain** an extra letter when they add **ed** and **ing** at the end.

For example: picnic   picnic**k**ing

1 Add **ed** and **ing** to the words below.

    a frolic   **d** panic

    b magic   **e** traffic

    c mimic

Lose one or more letters

2 Correct the words in **bold** in the sentences below.

For example: the female tiger is a **tigress**

    a The **enter** to the stadium was closed.

    b Shagusta's startled **exclaim** made us all jump.

    c The spectators thought the accident was **humour**.

    d Try to master the correct **pronounce** of the words.

    e Aaron has become very skilled at **carpenter**.

    f The alien vehicle was **cylinder** in shape.

    g Does Sharon really think she is **glamour**?

    h Yasar gave a **vigour** demonstration of gymnastics.

    i Carrying that heavy pack will be a big **hinder.**

    j The robot threatened to **vapour** everyone.

> **carpentry   cylindrical   entrance**
> **exclamation   glamorous   hindrance**
> **humorous   pronunciation**
> **vaporize (or vaporise)   vigorous**

Animal adjectives

'Animal' adjectives are not always obvious.

Most of them come from Latin names.

For example: Something that is bee-like is **apian.**

The Latin word for bee is **apis**.

Some of these adjectives are not used very often.

1 Match the pictures below to the adjectives. You may have to refer to a dictionary for some of them.

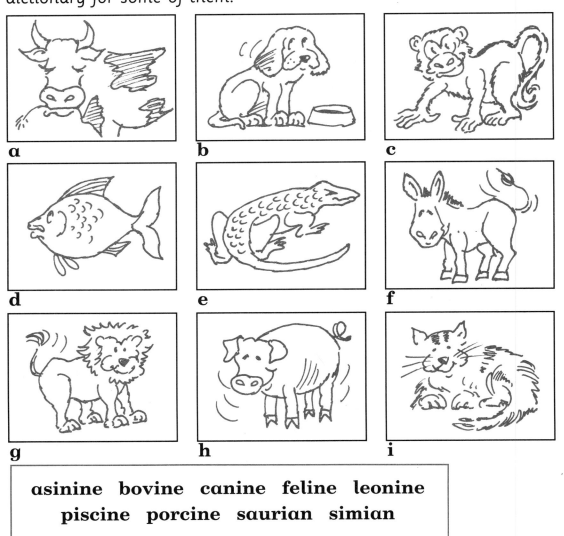

asinine bovine canine feline leonine
piscine porcine saurian simian

al ful wel til

1 In the word square below there are ten words which begin with **al**, five words which end in **ful**, two words which begin with **wel** and one word which ends in **til**.

Identify and complete the words.

l	c	w	o	n	d	e	r	m	b
a	w	g	i	m	o	n	y	i	i
w	a	y	s	c	o	m	e	g	n
l	h	u	s	e	k	m	s	h	o
l	i	m	f	a	r	e	n	t	o
w	g	m	c	h	e	e	r	y	c
p	n	q	r	s	u	n	t	b	o
u	v	c	o	m	e	w	x	u	h
z	k	a	l	i	n	e	y	m	o
t	e	r	n	a	t	i	v	e	l

albino album alcohol align alimony alkaline
almighty alms alternative always awful cheerful
lawful until useful welcome welfare wonderful

Word mix 4

1 Use the words in the box to complete the sentences below. Write them in your book.

a Strain the vegetables through a _ _ _ _ _ _ _ r.

b The windscreen is best cleaned with a c _ _ _ _ _ s leather.

c The messenger collapsed from f _ _ _ _ _ e.

d Tom had difficulty with his p _ _ _ _ _ _ _ _ _ _ _ n of French words.

e Place all the numbers in s _ q _ _ _ _ _ , starting now.

f The car's i _ _ _ _ _ _ _ _ s were not working at the time.

g The author wrote a pr _ _ _ _ _ _ and an ep _ _ _ _ _ _ in the book.

h An old soldier never v _ _ _ _ _ ee _ _ for anything.

i Stay on guard and be particularly w _ _ _ _ _ _ l tonight.

j Two rolls of Christmas w _ _ p _ _ _ _ paper, please.

k Lynne is a p _ _ _ _ _ _ _ t and never expects any happy events.

**chamois   colander   epilogue   fatigue
indicators   pessimist   prologue
pronunciation   sequence   volunteers
watchful   wrapping**

Suffixes

The endings of some words have particular meanings.

For example:

The apple is **eatable** means that the apple can be eaten.
The **suffix** is **able**.

A little goose is called a **gosling**.
The suffix is **ling**.

A place for sleeping is a **dormitory**.
The suffix is **ory**.

1 Attach one of the suffixes below to the part-words.

able	ible	ant	et	ette	fy
icle	less	ling	ock	ory	ous

a extremely well known   fam _ _ _
b place where things are made   fact _ _ _
c little hill   hill _ _ _
d little duck   duck _ _ _ _
e little cigar   cigar _ _ _ _
f very little bit   part _ _ _ _
g can be moved   mov _ _ _ _
h takes no care at all   care _ _ _ _
i make bigger   magni _ _
j for keepsakes around one's neck lock _ _
k amazing, astounding   incred _ _ _ _
l attends people   attend _ _ _

Suffixes 2

1 The part-words below end in: **et**, **el**, **ette**, **ing**, **icle**, **kin**, **let** or **ule**. The endings, however, have been misplaced. Put them back correctly.

a book**ette**   **i** ru**let**
b brace**kin**   **j** statu**let**
c isl**ing**   **k** pork**lel**
d ros**icle**   **l** eag**kin**
e cub**ing**   **m** mani**ette**
f sapl**el**   **n** nap**et**
g pip**icle**   **o** epaul**ule**
h bri**qule**

2 The endings on the words below are missing altogether and the part-words are scrambled. Begin each word with the two letters in **bold**.

a ob**gl**   **g** ron**co**
b ms**da**   **h** ng**cy**
c ck**lo**   **i** ick**ch**
d **lo**w   **j** ng**ri**
e rl**da**   **k** leds**g**
f lec**mo**   **l** vu**ri**

Astrology

Many people believe that it is possible to describe a person's character according to their sign of the Zodiac.

1 Find the following signs of the Zodiac in the word square. You will have to do some research.

a the ram **e** the lion **i** the archer

b the bull **f** the virgin **j** the goat

c the twins **g** the balance or scales **k** the water carrier

d the crab **h** the scorpion **l** the fishes

g	v	i	r	g	o	x	r	f	z	a	b	f	p
p	s	u	n	t	a	u	r	u	s	s	i	u	l
r	a	w	p	f	m	g	g	b	s	t	r	t	a
e	g	q	t	w	r	e	f	z	p	r	t	u	n
d	i	w	u	c	f	m	g	k	a	o	h	r	e
i	t	p	e	a	l	i	b	r	a	l	d	e	t
c	t	i	c	n	r	n	b	a	r	o	a	c	s
t	a	s	e	c	d	i	g	f	i	g	y	a	t
i	r	c	l	e	o	e	u	h	e	y	k	i	s
o	i	e	z	r	i	l	n	s	s	z	j	d	a
n	u	s	y	m	o	z	q	p	m	r	s	o	c
s	s	c	o	r	p	i	o	u	t	o	w	z	e
e	c	a	p	r	i	c	o	r	n	v	o	x	r
b	h	o	r	o	s	c	o	p	e	y	z	n	o
x	t	f	e	s	t	a	r	s	z	a	e	c	f

uni

uni comes from the Latin word for **one**.

1 Decode the words below and match them with their correct meanings.

}{ = uni   @ = a   * = e   <> = i   >< = o

All other letters are themselves.

a }{ s >< n

b }{ f >< r m

c }{ t

d }{ l @ t * r @ l

e }{ q u *

f }{ f <> c @ t <> >< n

g }{ c y c l *

h }{ s * x

i }{ n <> v * r s @ l

j }{ >< n

k }{ c >< r n

l }{ f >< r m <> t y

m }{ v * r s <> t y

n }{ t * d

1 only one like it	**6** it happened to East Germany and West Germany	**11** name used by some football teams
2 place of higher education	**7** soldiers wear one	**12** all together - in
3 belongs to everyone	**8** joined together	**13** just one
4 action by one person or group	**9** for men and women	**14** fabulous horse with one horn
5 all looking alike	**10** one wheeled cycle	

bi

In some words, **bi** comes from the Latin word for two.

For example: bicentenary   biceps   bicycle   bifocal

binoculars   biped   biplane   biscuit

1   Find the answers to the clues below.] [stands for **bi**.
The rest of the word has been slightly scrambled.

a	an aeroplane with two wings	] [enalp
b	marrying whilst married to someone else	] [ymag
c	two hundred years' anniversary	] [nyranecte
d	cut in two	] [tces
e	two-legged	] [dep
f	arm muscles	] [spec
g	two-wheeled vehicle	] [elcyc
h	dual function spectacles	] [lacofs
i	twice-baked cookie	] [tiucs
j	for viewing long distances	] [sralucon

2   In the following sentences **bi** does not mean two.
Complete the sentences.

a The apples tasted extremely b _ _ _ _ r.

b We ate and drank at the new b _ _ _ _ o .

c A female dog is called a b _ _ _ h.

d Extra reading is suggested in the
b _ _ _ _ _ _ _ _ _ _ y.

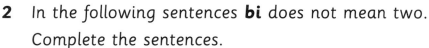

bibliography   bistro   bitch   bitter

tri quad

*tri comes from the Latin word for **three**.*

1 Find the **tri** and **quad** words in the quadrilateral below. All the letters of the **tr** words are in △ [triangles]. All the letters of the **quad** words are in ☐ [squares]. The letters are in sequence. Match them with their meanings below.

a quarter of a circle's circumference

b fossil sea-creature

c committee of three

d three- pronged weapon

e four babies born at the same time

f French flag

g four-legged animal

h three related stories

i three-legged stand

j algebraic equation

k four-sided courtyard

q	t△	q	u	a	d	r	a	t△	i	c	q
u	r△	u	y△	g△	o△	l△	i△	r△	t△	q	u
a	i△	a	q	f	u	t	q	i△	r△	u	a
d	c△	d	t	t△	q	u	u	l△	i△	t	d
r	o△	r	q	n△				o△	b△	q	r
a	l△	a	t	e△				b△	u△	t	u
n	o△	n	q	d△				i△	n△	u	p
g	u△	t△	r△	i△	p△	o△	d△	t△	a△	t	l
l	r△	u	q	r△	u	t	q	e△	l△	q	e
e	u	u	t	t△	q	t	u	t	q	u	t
u	q	d	e	p	u	r	d	a	u	q	s

2 Write three sentences to define the words below.

a quince

b quinine

c quintet

38

cent micro mill

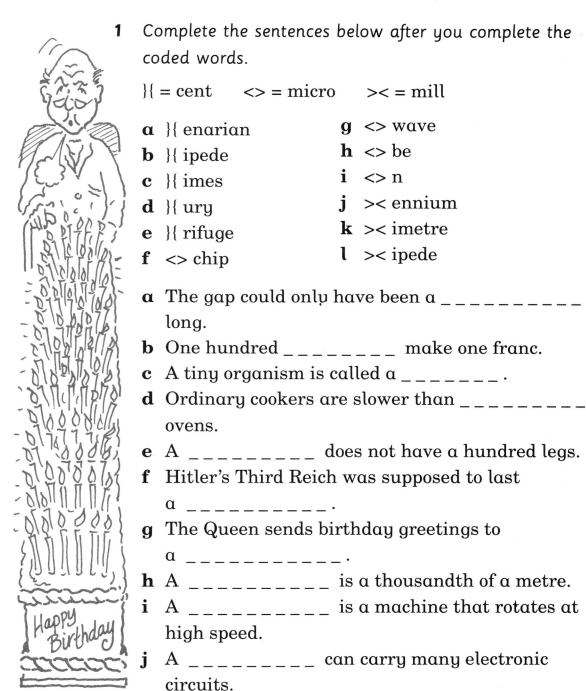

1 Complete the sentences below after you complete the coded words.

}{ = cent   <> = micro   >< = mill

a }{ enarian
b }{ ipede
c }{ imes
d }{ ury
e }{ rifuge
f <> chip

g <> wave
h <> be
i <> n
j >< ennium
k >< imetre
l >< ipede

a The gap could only have been a _ _ _ _ _ _ _ _ _ _ long.
b One hundred _ _ _ _ _ _ _ _ make one franc.
c A tiny organism is called a _ _ _ _ _ _ _ .
d Ordinary cookers are slower than _ _ _ _ _ _ _ _ _ ovens.
e A _ _ _ _ _ _ _ _ _ does not have a hundred legs.
f Hitler's Third Reich was supposed to last
a _ _ _ _ _ _ _ _ _ _ .
g The Queen sends birthday greetings to
a _ _ _ _ _ _ _ _ _ _ .
h A _ _ _ _ _ _ _ _ _ _ is a thousandth of a metre.
i A _ _ _ _ _ _ _ _ _ _ is a machine that rotates at
high speed.
j A _ _ _ _ _ _ _ _ _ can carry many electronic
circuits.

Word mix 5

1 Find the words to fit the clues.

a   dinosaurs are   f _ _

b   just become a soldier!   r _ _

c   may contain historic items   m _ _

d   meaningless gabble   g _ _

e   burdensome   o _ _

f   working together for a purpose   l _ _

g   don't trade with that country   e _ _

h   school for little children   k _ _

i   don't know what to do in one   q _ _

j   out of reach and out of sight   b _ _

k   writes for a newspaper   j _ _

l   here, there, everywhere   u _ _

m   liquid sets   c _ _

n   feeling sick?   n _ _

o   two minds talking and not a word   t _ _

p   homes of plants and animals   h _ _

q   up-and-down toy on a string   y _ _

r   experiments on living creatures   v _ _

**beyond   congeal   embargo   fossils   gibberish
habitat   journalist   kindergarten   liaison
museum   nausea   onerous   quandary   recruit
telepathy   ubiquitous   vivisection   yo-yo**

Words for today

1 Copy and complete the crossword below or write down the answers to the clues.

Clues across

3 newspapers, TV and radio
5 support and reserve
7 airliner with a trunk
8 stop shooting
9 petroleum pollution
13 plastic packing and insulation
17 produces nuclear power
18 space traveller
19 fast food restaurant
20 searches to find

Clues down

1 helicopter pad
2 brief swimsuit
4 cushioned craft
6 South African separation
10 wizard with numbers
11 controls perspiration
12 the computer, not the disk
14 in orbit
15 the disk, not the computer
16 M1, M4, M25?

Adopted words

1 Copy and complete the crossword below or write down the answers to the clues.

Clues across	Adopted from	Clues down	Adopted from
3 one level house	Gujarati	**1** divided skirt	French
7 wash your hair	Hindi	**2** fashion shop	French
8 martial art	Japanese	**4** material picture	French
9 oriental market	Persian	**5** short-hooded coat	Eskimo
11 dance hall	French	**6** not allowed	Tongan
12 horsey event	Hindi	**8** denim trousers	French
15 beef snack in a bun	German	**10** comes back in Oz	Aboriginal
16 open pie with various toppings	Italian	**11** jeans' material	French
		13 breakfast food	Swiss (German)
		14 bed cover	French

American spellings

The English language is spoken in America but many words are spelt differently.

1 The English versions of the words below end in **our**. Convert the following American spellings to English spellings.

    a color   **b** flavor   **c** honor

2 English versions of the following words end in **ise**. Convert these words to their English spelling. Many people in the UK already use the **ize** version.

    a advertize   **b** deputize   **c** recognize

3 Using a dictionary to help you, convert these American spellings to English spellings.

    a alright   **h** connexion
    b center   **i** fuze
    c counselor   **j** jewelry
    d anesthetic   **k** gray
    e chiseled   **l** maneuver
    f defense   **m** humor
    g catalog   **n** odor

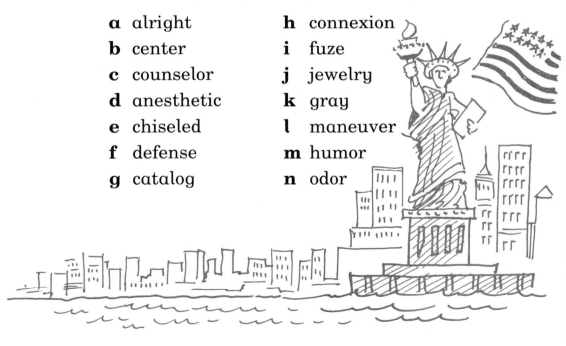

Signing off

1 Use the words in the box to find the words below.

  a enforces rules in cricket   u _ _ _

  b to do with race   e _ _ _

  c to do with fire   i _ _ _

  d extreme love of country   n _ _ _

  e corpse revived by voodoo   z _ _ _

  f to do with the ear   a _ _ _

  g passenger building at airport   t _ _ _

  h US name for paraffin   k _ _ _

  i hatred of foreigners   x _ _ _

  j swing to and fro   o _ _ _

  k essential in food   v _ _ _

  l to do with missiles   b _ _ _

  m pregnancy   g _ _ _

  n home   d _ _ _

  o sour and made from milk   y _ _ _

  p home on wheels   c _ _ _

  q speech understood only by a group   j _ _ _

**aural ballistic caravan domicile
ethnic gestation incendiary jargon
kerosene nationalism oscillate
terminal umpire vitamin
xenophobia yoghurt zombie**

Word list

à la carte
abbreviation
ability
able
absolute
accountant
accuracy
accurate
acid
acknowledge
acne
acorn
acoustic
acquaintance
acquire
acquisition
acquittal
acre
acrid
acrimonious
acronym
acrylic
activate
actuary
ad infinitum
adjective
adverb
aerated
aerial
aerobics
aerodrome
aerodynamics
aeroplane
aghast
albino
album
alcohol
alias
align
alimony
alkaline

allergy
almighty
alms
alternative
altitude
always
amphibian
anachronism
anaesthetic
anagram
analogy
analyse
ancient
android
anecdote
angular
animation
annihilate
anonymous
anorak
answerphone
antecedent
antediluvian
anthem
anthology
antidote
antiseptic
antonyms
anxiety
anxious
anybody
apartheid
ape-like
application
Aquarius
(the water
carrier)
Aries (the
ram)
armies
artefact

artery
arthritis
articulated
artificial
artillery
ascertain
ascetic
asexual
asinine
askance
asparagus
asphalt
asphyxia
aspidistra
aspirin
assets
asterisk
asteroid
asthma
astronaut
asylum
atmosphere
attendant
audacious
audio
audit
auditor
augment
aural
aureole
auspices
austere
authentic
authority
automatic
autumn
available
awful
axes
axis

backup
bacteria
ballad
ballerina
ballistic
baton
bazaar
beautiful
benefit
beyond
biblical
bibliography
bicentenary
biceps
bicycle
bifocal
bigamy
bikini
bimbo
binoculars
biodegradable
bionic
biopsy
biped
biplane
biscuit
bisect
bistro
bitch
bitter
blitzkrieg
blues
bon voyage
booklet
boomerang
boutique
bovine
bracelet
braces
brackets
bric-à-brac

briquette
budget
bullish
bungalow
bureau
bureaux
(bureaus)
business
busker
bustle
butcher

café au lait
cafeteria
caffeine
calculator
cancel
cancellation
Cancer (the
crab)
candid
candidate
canine
canister
cannibal
cantankerous
canyon
Capricorn
(the goat)
capsize
caravan
careful
careless
carpentry
(carpenter)
cash
  dispenser
catlike
catty
cavity
ceasefire

centime
centipede
centrifuge
century
chamois
cheerful
cherub
cherubim
(cherubs)
chicken
choreography
chronicle
cigarette
circle
circular
cleanliness
cocoa
colander
collage
colon &
  semicolon
column
comedian
comma
commission
compre-
  hensive
condemn
congeal
conjunction
conjuror
constable
constituents
contemporary
contract
contralto
cordon bleu
coronary
coronet
corporation
coup

courteous
crescendo
criticism
cruel
cruelty
cubicle
culottes
curricula
(curriculums)
curriculum
curtain
customary
cygnet
cylindrical
(cylinder)

damsel
darling
decency
decent
decision
decisive
decompose
deliberate
delight
demon-
    stration
denim
deodorant
department
descant
descend
detergent
deuce
diameter
dictionary
dictum
diesel
diminutive
direction
directive
director
directory
discord

discotheque
disguise
disintegrated
dismal
distant
divisions
doggy
domicile
doubt
dozen
draughts
(checkers)
duckling
ducks
duet
dungeon
duvet
dyslexia

eaglet
eatable
ECU
    (European
    Currency
    Unit)
efficiently
effluent
elastic
elephantine
elite
embargo
empire
encore
energetic
energy
entrance
(enter)
epaulette
epilogue
epistle
equine
error
ethnic
Eureka!

exclamation
    mark (or
    interjection)
exclamation
    (exclaim)
exhaust
expedi-
    tionary
expenditure
extract
factory
falsetto
famous
fanfare
farce
fatigue
feline
feminine
    (gender)
ferocity
feud
feudal
fierce
finale
fishy
fleur-de-lys
flora
florae
(floras)
fool
footlights
formula
formulae
(formulas)
fossils
foxy
friend
frolicking
fungi
fungus
funnel

gala
gallery

gargantuan
Gemini (the
    heavenly
    twins)
gendarme
genera
generosity
genus
geology
gestation
gibberish
glamorous
glazier
global
    warming
globule
gloves
gnarled
goods
gosling
greasepaint
grouse
gymkhana
gymnasia
(gymnasiums)
gymnasium
gypsies
(gipsies)

habit
habitat
hamburger
handsome
hardware
harmony
height
helicopter
heliport
hillock
hindrance
holocaust
homonyms
homosexual
horrible

horses
horsey
hovercraft
humorous
hymn
hypnotise
    (ize)

illusionist
immense
impedimenta
impressionist
incendiary
incinerator
income
incredible
inflatable
inflation
inquisition
insurance
interest
interference
intermittent
investment
invisible
islet

jargon
jazz
jealousy
jeans
joint
journalist
judo
jumbo jet
justice

kerosene
kindergarten
kitten
knowledge

laugh
laughter

leisure
Leo (the
    Lion)
leonine
leopard
leotard
leukaemia
liabilities
liaison
Libra (the
    Scales)
lieutenant
limelight
locket
lunacy
luncheon

magicking
magnificent
magnify
mal de mer
malignant
manana
(tomorrow)
manikin
manipulate
man-
    slaughter
marathon
marionette
mascara
masculine
    (gender)
maternity
measles
mechanical
media
medicine
melodrama
melody
menstruation
mensuration
mental
mentality

mention
menu
mesmerise
  (ize)
metaphor
metropolitan
microbe
microchip
micron
microscope
microwave
millennium
millimetre
millipede
mimicking
mnemonic
molecule
monologue
monoplane
morgue
mortgage
motorway
movable
muesli
mulish
murder
museum

napkin
nationalism
nausea
Nazi
neighbours
nerve
neuter
  (gender)
news
nicotine
nom de
  plume
nostalgic
novelty

oases

oasis
octopi
  (octopuses)
octopus
oil slick
onerous
onomatopoeia
opera
opportunity
optima
  (optimums)
optimum
orchestra
organic
orphan
oscillate
overture
owlet
owlish
ozone layer

panel
panicking
parade
particle
pedestrian
pendulum
pension
perforation
pessimist
pesticide
petroleum
phenomena
phenomenon
philately
philosophy
photograph
photography
phrase
physical
pianos
pickets
picnic
picnicking

pigeon
piggish
pincers
pipette
Pisces (the
  fishes)
piscine
pizza
plateau
plateaux
  (plateaus)
platypi
  (platypuses)
platypus
pneumatic
pneumonia
polyhedra
  (polyhedrons)
polyhedron
polystyrene
polythene
poor
porcine
porkling
possible
poverty
precaution
precious
precipice
precision
prefabricated
pregnant
prehistoric
premature
premises
preparation
preposition
presence
presentation
preservation
president
prestige
presume
pretence

prevention
prima
  donna
probability
probation
probe
problem
procession
prodigy
product
profession
proficiency
profit
program
prologue
promenade
prompter
pronoun
pronunc-
  iation
proof
propaganda
property
prophecy
prophesy
prophet
proportion
proprietor
proscenium
prosecution
prosperity
prosperous
protractor
proverb
psychology
puppet

quadrangle
quadrant
quadratic
quadruped
quadruplets
quandary
quarrel

quince
quinine
quintet

racquet
  (racket)
radiation
radii
  (radiuses)
radioactivity
radius
rain forests
reactor
real
realism
realistic
reality
recipe
reckoning
recruit
recurring
refugees
regatta
rehearsal
reindeer
reliable
remote
  control
rendezvous
repetition
reptilian
requiem
resigned
retrospect
rhapsody
rheumatism
rhinoceros
rhodo-
  dendron
rhombus
rhubarb
rhumba
rhyme
rhythm

ringlet
rivulet
rock-and-
  roll
rosette
rostra
  (rostrums)
rostrum
routine

Sagittarius
  (the
  archer)
salmon
sapling
satellite
scanner
scenery
scenic
scissors
score
Scorpio
  (the
  scorpion)
script
seasonal
securities
seedling
self-service
senator
seniority
sensation
sensible
sensitive
sensor
sentimental
sequence
seraph
seraphim
  (seraphs)
serenade
sewage
  disposal
shampoo

sheep
shelves
shopping
  precinct
short
shortage
shovel
simian
similes
simple
simplicity
singular
slapstick
smithereens
snaky
socks
solemn
sonata
soprano
space
specimen
spectacles
stalagmite
statuette
staunch
steadfast
stereophonic
Stock
  Exchange
stockbroker
strata
stratum
substantial
suds
Sun (Sol)
surgeon
syllabi
syllabus
symphony
symptoms
synonyms

tabloid
taboo

tassel
tattoo
Taurus (the
  bull)
telepathy
tenacious
tenor
terminal
terracotta
terra firma
terrible
terrified
territory
terror
terrorist
texture
theatrical
theodolite
thermometer
thieves
thought
throat
tidings
tigress
toes
tomatoes
tombstone
tongs
topical
toxic
trafficking
tragedy
transplant
transport
treble
tremulous
tribunal
tricolour
trident
trilobite
trilogy
tripod
trophies
truncheon

turkeys
ubiquitous
umpire
unaminity
understudy
unicorn
unicycle
unification
uniform
uniformity
unilateral
union
unique
unisex
unison
unitarian
united
unity
universal
university
until
useful

vacancy
vague
vain
valour
valuable
vandal
vanity
vaporize (or
  vaporise)
ventriloquist
verbatim
viaduct
vice versa
view
vigorous
Virgo (the
  virgin)
viscount
vivacious
vivid
vivisection

vocal
voice
volunteers
vowel

warrant
watchful
welcome
welfare
wit
witches
witty
wolfish
wonderful
wool
woollen
wrapping
wreaked
wrist

xenophobia
xylophone

yeoman
yodel
yoghurt
yoyo

zeal
Zodiac
zombie

**USA
spellings**
alright
anesthetic

catolog
center
chiseled
color
connexion
counselor

defense
deputize

flavor
funneled
fuze

gray

honor
humor

jewelry

maneuver

odor

pretense

recognize

specter

theater
thru
tonite